MIDNIGHT MUNCHIES

HÄGAR

THE HORRIBLE BY DIK BROWNE

MIDNIGHT MUNCHIES

tempo
books
GROSSET & DUNLAP
A Filmways Company
Publishers • New York

HAGAR THE HORRIBLE: MIDNIGHT MUNCHIES

Copyright © 1980, 1982 by King Features Syndicate, Inc.

All Rights Reserved
ISBN: 0-448-16993-2
An Ace Tempo Original
Tempo Books is registered in the U.S. Patent Office
Printed in the United States of America
Published simultaneously in Canada

9-29
DIK BROWNE

ER.. AFTER-DINNER MINT, SIR?

WHAT DO YOU MEAN — "BACK UP"?!!

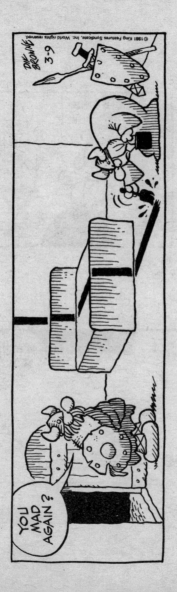

HÄGAR
the Horrible
By Dik Browne

Get carried away by America's favorite Viking!

☐ 12641-9   **HAGAR THE HORRIBLE #1** $1.25

☐ 12642-7   **HAGAR THE HORRIBLE #2** $1.50

☐ 12643-5   **HAGAR THE HORRIBLE #3:**
ON THE LOOSE $1.50

☐ 12644-3   **HAGAR THE HORRIBLE #4:**
THE BRUTISH ARE COMING $1.50

☐ 12649-4   **HAGAR THE HORRIBLE #5:**
ON THE RACK $1.50

☐ 17114-7   **HAGAR THE HORRIBLE #7:**
HAGAR'S KNIGHT OUT $1.25
